Sam's Flood Plan

Simon Cheshire ▪ Javier Jouquin

OXFORD
UNIVERSITY PRESS

Sam was a boy who worried a lot.
He worried about things at school.
He worried about things at home.
He worried about endangered animals
and global warming.

"Don't worry so much, Sam," said his mum. "Worrying won't change things." Sam knew that Mum was right but he worried anyway.

One of the things Sam worried about was the river. It ran across the field behind Sam's house. Sam was worried about the river rising and causing a flood.

He saw news reports on TV about floods. He saw streets and houses filled with muddy water. Nothing worried Sam more than that river. He worried every time it rained.

Sam read some books from the school library about floods. He also found some pages on the Internet. They told him what to do if there was a flood.

Flood Action

- Turn off the water and power supply.
- Plug the sinks so that no dirty water can come up through the plug holes.
- Seal the windows and doors to stop water getting in.
- Move items upstairs so they don't get damaged if water does get in.
- Listen to the radio in case there is important news.

So Sam made a flood plan.

Sam's Flood Plan

Our house

Turn off the water and power supply.

Plug the sinks.

Seal the windows
and doors.

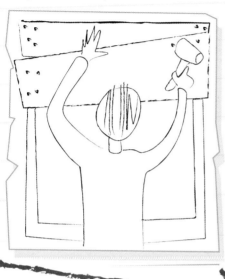

Move items
upstairs.

Listen to the news.

One day, during the summer, the rain fell like water poured from a bucket. It rained and rained and didn't stop for days. The river began to rise.

"Don't worry, Sam," said Mum. "The rain will stop soon."

The rain didn't stop. The river rose. Water crawled slowly across the field. It spread out towards the houses.

Sam was very worried. He gave a copy of his flood plan to every house in the street.

Soon the water reached Sam's garden.
"We didn't think this would happen!"
cried Dad.
"What shall we do?" cried Mum.

Sam knew just what to do. It was
time to put his flood plan into action!

Sam told his mum and dad what to do.

1 Turn off the water, electricity and gas.

2 Put plugs in the sinks.

3 Move food and small items upstairs.

14

Still the rain didn't stop. The water spread closer to Sam's house. "Don't worry," Sam told his parents. "The water won't get in if we follow my flood plan."

Next Sam told his parents:

4 Fetch sheets of wood from the garage.

5 Seal around the windows and doors. Nail wood tight across the doorways.

6 Turn on the radio in case there is important news.

Mum and Dad did exactly as Sam told them.

Soon, the flood water reached the house. It came up against the walls and the sealed doors. Little leaks trickled into the kitchen through the door. Mum mopped up the floor. But the water didn't come in anywhere else

Finally, it stopped raining.

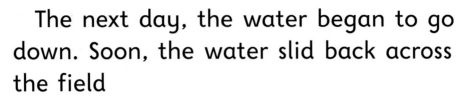

The next day, the water began to go down. Soon, the water slid back across the field

Sam, Mum and Dad came out and looked around the street. None of the houses had been flooded. The water had been kept out – because of Sam's Flood Plan.

"Sam!" everyone called. "You're a hero! Without your plan our homes would have been wrecked!"

"So I was right to worry," said Sam, grinning.

"No," said Mum. "You were right to think ahead. If you had just worried you would never have saved our house. You faced up to your worry by taking calm and sensible action."

Sam wasn't worried about floods any more. He knew what to do about them. Perhaps he could face up to all his other worries this way.

Retell the story

Flood facts

- In 1953 a very bad flood killed 300 people near London. Afterwards, the Thames Barrier was built across the river Thames to guard against flooding.

- Scientists think that global warming might bring more flooding.

- 5 centimetres of flood water can make a car float away!

- Heavy rains, called monsoons, cause flooding every year in some parts of Asia.

JOKE
Q: How do you cut the sea in half?
A: With a sea saw.